Honesty

THE HONEST WOODCUTTER

Adapted by Jennifer Boudart

Illustrated by Tammie Lyon

Copyright © 2002 Publications International, Ltd.
ISBN: 0-7853-4310-5
Leap Frog is a trademark of Publications International, Ltd.

There once was a woodcutter who lived with his wife and two children in a forest far from the nearest town. The woodcutter built his home with logs that he cut himself. The house was not big or fancy, but it was warm and dry. The family was not rich, but they were happy and lived comfortably.

One morning while eating breakfast, the family joked about what their lives would be like if they had lots of money. The woodcutter wished for a bigger house, his wife dreamed of eating from fine china plates, and the children imagined playing with all sorts of wonderful toys.

When breakfast ended, the woodcutter put on his hat, grabbed his ax, and headed to work. His family stood on the porch of the house and waved good-bye to him as he walked deep into the forest.

"I'll be home for dinner," called the woodcutter.

The woodcutter worked in the oldest part of the forest, where the trees grew tallest and thickest. These trees were also the hardest to chop down, but they were no problem for the woodcutter. He was the best around. The woodcutter simply sharpened his trusty old ax and went to work.

Soon wood chips flew through the air, and the forest echoed with the loud sound of the woodcutter's ax chopping. A little squirrel happened to be collecting nuts nearby, and she heard the noise of the woodcutter's ax. The squirrel went to see who was making all the noise and was amazed by how quickly the woodcutter chopped. She sat on a large pile of neatly stacked logs that the woodcutter had chopped earlier that morning. The woodcutter was so busy that he did not notice that the squirrel was sitting there. He thought only about cutting more wood so he could give his family all the things they wanted.

Each day the woodcutter worked until noon and then took a short break. He liked to walk to the edge of the river to eat lunch and have a cool drink of water.

One day, however, the woodcutter was so thirsty that he walked too quickly to the river to get a drink. He did not notice a rock that was right in his path.

"Yikes!" shouted the woodcutter as he tripped over the rock. His ax slipped and landed in the river.

The woodcutter looked into the river, hoping to see his ax, but it was no use! The ax was gone. Without his ax, the woodcutter could not chop wood and buy the things for his family. "What am I going to do?" cried the woodcutter.

Suddenly the river started to make noise. The sad woodcutter looked up and saw the water rising. Then the water grew arms and a head, and it started to talk to him! "I am the water sprite, a fairy of this river. Why are you so sad?"

After the woodcutter told him what had happened, the water sprite said, "Don't worry. I can help you. I'll go down to the bottom of the river to find your ax." In an instant the sprite was gone, and the river began to swirl and foam.

In a few moments, the water sprite appeared again. "Is this your ax?" he asked the woodcutter.

The woodcutter looked closely at the ax. It was made of pure silver! The woodcutter thought about taking it, but the ax did not belong to him. He knew it would be wrong to say it was his. Finally the woodcutter said, "I cannot take this ax. It is not mine."

The water sprite tossed the silver ax on the ground and said, "Very well, I'll look for your ax again."

Once again the sprite went down to the bottom of the river. When the water sprite returned after a few moments, he held an ax that was more magnificent than the first one. It was made of solid gold!

"This must be yours," said the sprite.

The woodcutter held the amazing gold ax for a moment. This ax could make him very rich. He could buy everything his family wanted. But the woodcutter gave the ax back to the sprite. "This is a fine ax," he explained. "But this ax is not mine either."

The water sprite smiled and said, "Let me look for it once more."

For a third time the sprite disappeared. When the sprite returned, he held another ax. This ax was not shiny at all, and the old handle was worn from use. The woodcutter smiled and said, "Ah yes! This is my ax."

The water sprite shook his head. "Are you sure you want this ax? The other two are so much finer!"

"Yes, but they are not mine," said the woodcutter.

The water sprite smiled. "Your ax is not worth much, but your honesty is. The silver and gold axes belong to me. Take them as a gift for telling the truth."

The woodcutter was very excited to have all three axes. He thanked the water sprite and decided that he would leave the forest early that day. Instead of going straight home, he went into town to go shopping.

The woodcutter could not wait to get to the store. When he arrived, he handed the fine axes to the store owner. The owner looked them over carefully and said, "These are the best axes that I have ever seen. I will gladly buy them from you."

The store owner was very generous. He gave the woodcutter a large sack of gold coins. Now the happy woodcutter was rich! He bought an armful of beautiful flowers and a set of fine china plates for his wife. He also bought a big bag of toys for his children.

The woodcutter had lots of gold left over and he carried it all back home with him. His wife and children were surprised that the woodcutter was home so early. They ran from the house to meet him.

When the woodcutter's wife saw the china plates and the flowers, she was so happy that tears came to her eyes. When the children saw the big bag filled with toys, they squealed with joy.

The woodcutter told his family all about the water sprite and all that had happened to him during the day. His family couldn't believe their ears!

That night, as he and his wife were putting their children to bed, his son looked up at him and asked, "Why did the water sprite give you all three axes?"

Then the woodcutter's daughter said, "Because you told the truth, right?"

"That's right," said the honest woodcutter, "because I told the truth."

Honesty

Honesty means telling the truth, and it is always best to tell the truth. Sometimes, though, telling the truth is not so easy to do. When the water sprite handed the woodcutter the silver and gold axes, it would have been easy for the woodcutter to say that they belonged to him. But because he told the truth, the water fairy gave the woodcutter both of the valuable axes as a reward.

The story of the honest woodcutter reminds us that when you tell the truth, things always work out for the best. It shows that honesty really is the best policy.